MW00354597

THE LOBSTER:
its life cycle

THE LOBSTER:
its life cycle

revised edition

By Herb Taylor

Pisces Books
New York, New York

PICTURE CREDITS

The front cover shows a red lobster, the product of a genetic experiment. The back cover shows a 15-day old larval lobster. Both photographs by the author. All of the photographs in this book were taken by the author, with the following exceptions: pages 2, 36, and 44 are by Lance Stewart; page 49 is by D. G. Wilder; page 69 is by Dan Sheehy; and pages 81 and 82 are by Ron Cutler.

Library of Congress Cataloging in Publication Data

Taylor, Herb, 1942-
    The lobster, its life cycle.

    Includes index.
    Summary: Text and illustrations describe each phase
of a lobster's life and discuss the detrimental effect
of overfishing on the lobster population and what is
being done to counter the problem.
        1. Lobsters— Juvenile literature. [1. Lobsters]
I. Title.

QL444.M33T39 1984   595.3'841   83-63355

ISBN 0-86636-022-0

Published by Pisces Book Co., Inc.
a division of The Photographic Book Co.
34 West 32 Street
New York, New York 10001

Note: This is a revised and expanded edition of *The Lobster: its life cycle*. The first edition was published in 1975. The New York Academy of Scien ces selected that edition as one of the best science books for young adults published that year.

10 9 8 7 6 5 4 3 2 1
Printed in Hong Kong

Acknowledgments

This book could not have been written without the help and cooperation of John T. Hughes, the Director of the Massachusetts Lobster Hatchery and Research Station on Martha's Vineyard. His knowledge of lobsters is only exceeded by his willingness to share what he has learned. Any errors that remain in this book, after his thoughtful reading, are mine entirely. Any insight into lobster behavior that the book may offer is due to his efforts. Thanks also to Tom Hotz and Fred Glodis.

Many thanks to Joan Mitchell, at Woods Hole Oceanographic Institution, for access to her notes, office, and laboratory, and for the time she so generously gave. Additional thanks to Jella Attema and Lori Stein.

Special thanks to Dan Sheehy at the University of Rhode Island for giving most generously of his time and for the opportunity to dive with him. Mention should also be made of Stanley Cobb, Akella Sastry, and Doug Wilcox.

Many thanks to Byron Porterfield at the New York Ocean Science Laboratory for his generosity and his help in making many of the photos in this book.

Thanks to John Lee at City College (NYC) for his patience and help in making the photomicrographs of the larval lobsters in this book one frantic morning in Woods Hole.

At the University of Connecticut, many thanks to Lance Stewart for sharing information gleaned from his many hours under water. Thanks, too, to Howard Weiss.

With the National Marine Fisheries Service at Woods Hole, Massachusetts, thanks to Richard Cooper and Joseph Uzmann for their help and cooperation.

With Maine's Department of Marine Resources at Boothbay Harbor, Maine, thanks to James Thomas for his time and efforts to help.

Special thanks to the researchers with the Fisheries Research Board of Canada (St. Andrews and New Brunswick), especially D. G. Wilder and D. J. Scarratt, and also H. H. Hord and Margot Schenk.

Thanks also go to the scientists and technicians that I did not contact directly, but whose papers proved invaluable, in particular, Jay S. Krouse, Leslie Scattergood, Richard Ford, and Jon Van Olst.

Finally, thanks to Cora Sibal, Richard Liu, Linda Weinraub, Larry Marquez, Erlinda Dinteman, Charlene Sison, Lou Waryncia, and the rest of the staff at PBC for all their help in putting this revised edition together.

— Herb Taylor

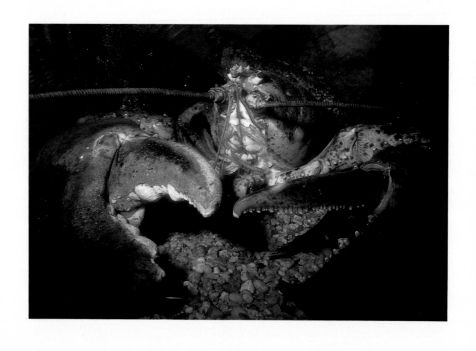

Contents

Foreword

by JOHN T. HUGHES
Massachusetts Lobster Hatchery and Research Station, Martha's Vineyard

The Maine lobster *(Homarus americanus)* is the most valuable marine resource landed in New England. Even though there has been a lobster fishery in the coastal waters of the Northwest Atlantic for more than three centuries, there has been very little written about the lobster's natural history, the expanse of the commercial populations, fishing methods, costs, and what the fishermen themselves think about the future of the lobster industry.

Marine scientists from Canada and the United States have been studying the lobster for many years. They are worried about the reported decline in the catch, and they are making joint efforts to develop a management program to ensure a continued supply of lobsters. Yet, at present, there are no federal or international laws pertaining to the lobster fishery.

The aquaculture of lobster is on the threshold of reality. It may one day solve the problem of a dwindling supply and an increasing demand. Marine biologists have been able to mate lobsters in the laboratory and select parents for desired characteristics, such as fast growth and large claws and tails. In the wild it takes eight years for a lobster to reach one pound, but in the laboratory lobsters have reached the same weight in less than two years.

Enough is known about the biology and life cycle of lobsters to start a commercial pilot plant operation. Some feel that in the near future it will be possible to raise lobsters profitably, on a large scale, as chickens are raised.

Soon perhaps, instead of only taking lobsters, and other marine resources, man will be farming, cultivating, and harvesting crops and livestock in the world's oceans.

Herb Taylor has done his homework before writing this book and his photographs help tell the lobster's story.

1

The Lobster's Background

Yes, a blue lobster! And red ones, white ones, and others in combinations of colors exist too. Strange-colored lobsters are sometimes found in the wild, but the blue lobster on the facing page and the other brightly colored lobsters on the following pages are in a marine laboratory in Massachusetts. There scientists are raising lobsters, with normal and abnormal pigmentation, to understand better how the animal lives in the wild, and to find methods of raising large numbers of lobsters on underwater farms. You will learn more about the work these and other scientists are doing with lobsters in Chapter 5 and 6.

Homarus americanus is the name scientists give to this common lobster of the east coast of North America. The complicated two-part name is necessary to avoid confusing it with the many other animals around the world that are also called lobsters. In Chapter 7, you will see some of the animals related to *H. americanus*, see where they live, and how similar their lives are.

This blue lobster was the result of a selective breeding experiment. Blue lobsters are found in the wild only on rare occasions.

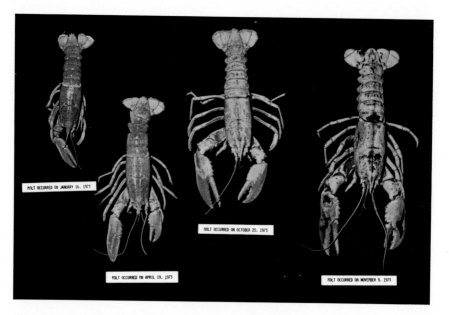

These are the cast-off shells of a lobster and the dates of its last four molts. The progression shows the process of growth and regeneration. Growth is dependent on many factors: diet, water temperature, space, and competition are a few. This animal's growth was hindered by the fact that it was regenerating a claw. Note that in three molts the regenerated claw is the same size as the normal one. Note, too, the general deterioration of the cast-off shells from molt to molt. During the last molt the animal died from an unknown cause.

Well Known Creature

It is strange that around the world, lobsters are the best known and easiest to recognize of all the marine invertebrates (animals without backbones), because almost everyone has seen a lobster even if only in a tank at a fish store or restaurant. But until recently, very little was known about lobsters, and in the past ten years man's knowledge of the animal has increased tenfold. Because lobsters are used around the world as food, man is very interested in learning yet more about these creatures that wear their skeletons on the outside of their bodies.

12

This lobster has recently lost its ripper claw and right antenna, but has started the process of regenerating its lost appendages. Its claw is just a pink bud now, and its antenna is a tiny pink coil, but after the animal's next molt both will be enlarged and hardened. Its left antenna, which was just lost, will have a coiled bud after that molt.

Exoskeleton

Their shell, called their exoskeleton, gives their bodies shape just as the bones inside birds or land animals give their bodies shape. Having a hard covering on the outside of their body offers good protection from enemies, but it does present some problems as the animal grows. Periodically throughout the animal's life it must shed its shell. As the lobster gets older its shell becomes tight, and if it is to grow any more it must cast off the restrictive shell. The shell the animal sheds is a perfect replica of the lobster itself—down to the tiniest detail.

Molting

It is quite a job for a lobster to struggle out of its glove of a covering. Sometimes lobsters struggle so hard and long that they wear them-

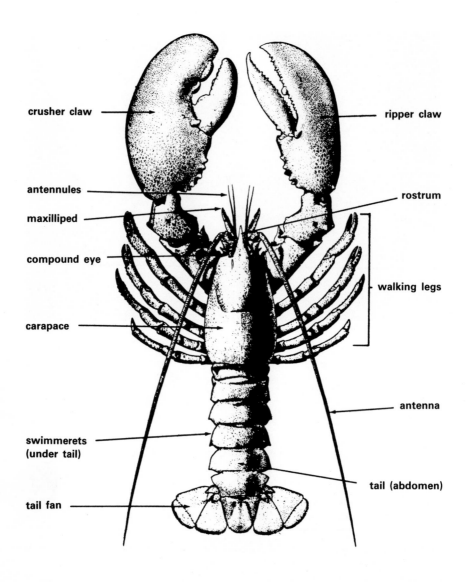

crusher claw

ripper claw

antennules

rostrum

maxilliped

compound eye

walking legs

carapace

antenna

swimmerets
(under tail)

tail (abdomen)

tail fan

In addition to the labels identifying the parts of the lobster, notice the segmentation of the tail (abdomen), and that all the appendages are jointed (some have as many as four joints). These two characteristics place the lobster in the phylum Arthropoda. *Its hard shell (actually its skeleton) places it in the class* Crustacea. *And because it has ten appendages (the large claws are included), it is in the order of animals called* Decapoda.

14

selves out and die. Most often though, if a lobster is having difficulty molting it can sacrifice a claw or leg to complete the molt. This is called "throwing a claw." Lobsters too can sometimes relinquish an appendage to their enemies while fighting, in order to escape.

To lose one of its body parts is not a permanent situation for a lobster. It has the amazing ability (along with lizards, starfish, and some other animals) to regenerate some of its body parts. If a lobster loses a claw to an enemy, a bud of a new claw will soon grow in its place. At the next molt the new claw will be about one-third normal size. By the second molt the claw will almost be back to normal. By the third molt only an expert will be able to tell that one of the claws had been regenerated.

Growth

The lobster's overall growth does suffer during the regeneration process though. All its energy seems to pour into getting the missing limb back to normal, so its growth and gain in body weight suffer. Lobsters can regenerate claws, walking legs, and antennae, but not any parts on their tail.

Lobsters are true products of their environment. Their growth, frequency of molt, and each phase of their life cycle are dependent on many many things that vary from place to place and from season to season. Two lobsters may weigh the same, but one taken from the rocky coast of New Brunswick and the other from a wreck off the New Jersey shore, will not be the same age. Neither will one living in 15 ft. (4.5 m.) of water on a breakwater in Long Island Sound, be the same age as one living in water 1,000 ft. (300 m.) deep in the canyons on the edge of the continental shelf.

Water temperature and food are the two most important factors affecting a lobster's growth and weight gain. But also important are: salinity, availability of shelter, frequency of regeneration, and even the kind of bottom they live on. In warm water they grow much faster than in cold, and naturally they do best when they can find all the food they need in a small search area.

Because of all the variables, by looking at any lobster it is virtually impossible to determine its age. Over the years though, scientists working with lobsters have come up with some estimates. They can say that a lobster taken from the wild in the 1–1½ pound

(453-680 grams) range, the size most often seen in restaurants and fish markets, took between six and eight years to attain that weight. More specific than that they cannot be, unless some of the variables are supplied.

Cannibalism

Much of what man knows about lobsters comes from laboratory experiments and from observing lobsters in small tanks. Whether lobsters behave the same way in tanks as they do in the wild is a question scientists are continually asking themselves. In the lab when a lobster molts, if another is near, the molted lobster is attacked and eaten. In the lab they are observed hoarding food from other lobsters in the tank. When young floating lobsters are confined to a small volume of water, they feed on each other. Some call it cannibalism.

Do these things happen in the wild? Do the unnatural conditions of the tank—the brightness, the lack of shelter, the crowding—put undue stress on lobsters? Does that cause them to modify their conduct in the same way land animals change when caged? Lately, some scientists have been studying lobsters in their natural environment to be able to answer some of these questions. They visit the lobster's dark cold world for short periods of time with skin-diving equipment and small submarines.

The material that follows about *Homarus americanus* was assembled from what some scientists have seen in the laboratory and what others have observed in the wild. Much is still to be learned. Scientists say that for every fact they learn about lobsters, they raise ten questions. That, though, is what science is all about—asking questions.

The underside of this calico lobster clearly shows the animal's swimmerets. The swimmerets serve various functions at different times in the animal's life. They are used for respiration, egg-holding (females), and, during the early part of the animal's life, locomotion. The first pair of swimmerets are different from the others—they are the animal's reproductive organs.

2

Life in the Water Column

In the summer months between June and September, as the waters off the coast of New England and the Canadian Maritime Provinces begin to warm to their maximum, the female lobster extrudes her eggs. Like everything else in the animal's life, the exact time is determined by the temperature of the water and the animal's own biological urgings.

Egg-laying time is a solitary period for the female. Her mate does not have to be present. Within her body she carries the sperm of their earlier meeting, that could have taken place up to a year before the time of egg laying. Female lobsters have the amazing ability to keep their mate's sperm alive and healthy within their bodies for long periods of time. So, any time from a month to a year after mating the female will lay her eggs.

Egg Laying

When she is ready, though, she rolls over onto her back, and supports herself on her two large claws and her tail, which she curls to form a pocket for the eggs. She assumes this awkward and vulnerable tripod position to keep the eggs from falling from her body as she lays them, and to eliminate any chance of bottom sediment contaminating the tiny eggs. She extrudes the eggs from the tiny openings at the base of the second pair of walking legs. As they flow down over the seminal receptacle, the stored sperm is released to fertilize the eggs. The now fertilized eggs continue down her body, moved by the action of her swimmerets, finally to be cemented in place under her tail by the sticky substance secreted with the eggs.

Depending on her size, the mass under the female can contain anywhere from 3,000 to 100,000 eggs, or more. Clinging to her, they look something like clusters of berries. Fishermen call lobsters with eggs, "berried" or "in berry."

A close look at newly extruded eggs. They adhere to each other and the female because a sticky substance is secreted along with them.

This lobster has just recently extruded its eggs. They are dark in color, meaning they will be carried by the lobster for almost another year before they hatch.

The eggs carried by this female lobster are ready to be hatched. Their golden-brown color shows that they are ripe and that as soon as water temperature and conditions are right, they will hatch.

A closer look at the ripe eggs reveals tiny blue spots on each. These are the developing eyes of the embryonic lobsters.

The newly laid eggs, each about 1/16 in. (approx. 2 mm.) in diameter, are dark green in color—almost black. Over the next year though, as cell division, yolk absorption, and embryo development take place within each egg they will ripen and begin to turn a golden brown. On close inspection two beautiful, iridescent blue spots can be seen. They are the developing eyes of the lobster.

She had held the sperm almost a year, and now she will carry the eggs on the underside of her tail for almost another year, giving her a total pregnancy of between 18 and 24 months. While the eggs cling to her, the regular beating of her swimmerets will supply the developing embryos with fresh oxygen-rich water. The constant beating also will keep them free of parasites and settling organisms. During this long period, she instinctively defends her brood from marauding fish and eels that attempt to steal her eggs. Through the cold winter she keeps her vigil.

This "berried" female is in the position normally taken while carrying eggs. By staying close to the bottom, with her tail curled underneath her body, she gives the eggs maximum protection.

Hatching

The following spring when the eggs have matured, she lines up with the current and slowly begins walking against it. She raises herself high on her walking legs and lifts her tail high off the bottom, and spreads her tail fan. Her swimmerets beat rapidly and she seems to vibrate slightly as the just-hatched larvae or fry (babies) leave their egg casings and float out from under her tail and toward the surface in a cloud.

Most hatching begins in the twilight hours and reaches its peak before midnight. This gives each tiny lobster the maximum number of hours of darkness to disperse and move away from the cloud of a thousand hatching babies. Packed together, the fry would make an easy target for predatory fish.

At the time of hatching the female walks slowly into the current, lifts her body high off the bottom, and raises her tail. Using her swimmerets, with gentle vibrations she shakes the hatching larvae loose.

A "berried" female will release bursts of fry several times each night, for as many nights as it takes all the tiny eggs to hatch. Usually though, within two weeks she completes the hatching.

Larvae in the Wild

Out from under their mother and by themselves for the first time, the lobster larvae are subject to all the perils of the sea. During this first month of their life, they will drift along uncontrollably. Carried by currents and moving up and down in the water column, they will be exposed to more danger and predators now than at any other time in their life.

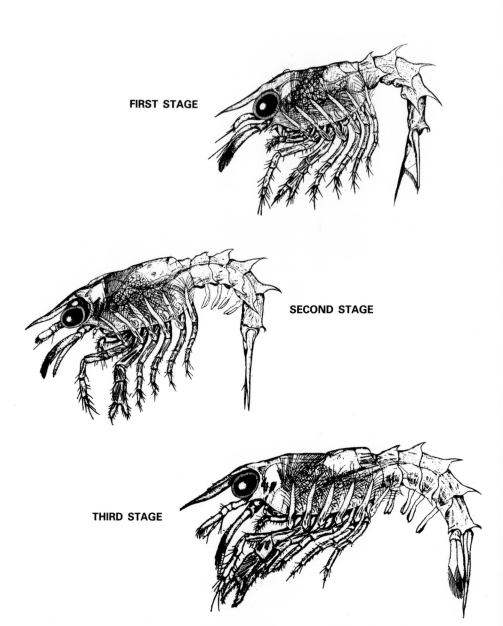

FIRST STAGE

SECOND STAGE

THIRD STAGE

These four drawings show the development lobster larvae undergo as they change from planktonic creatures to bottom dwellers. (Drawings from The American Lobster: a study of its habits and development *by Francis H. Herrick. Bulletin U.S. Fishery Commission 15:1—252, 1896.)*

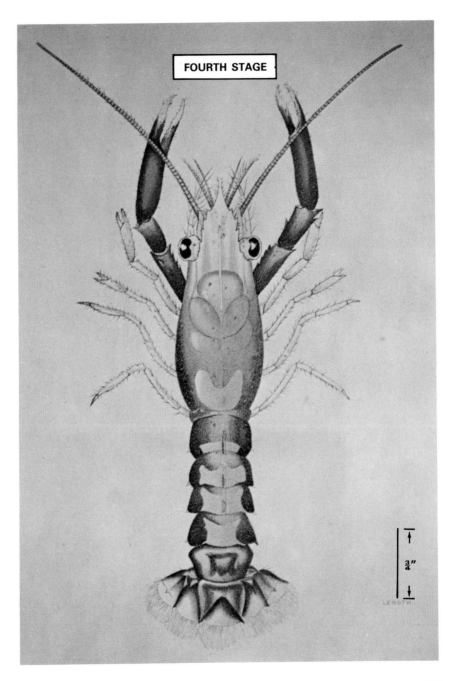

FOURTH STAGE

¾″ LENGTH

(Above). This first-stage lobster has only been free of its egg casing for about two days. Drifting through the water it will feed on other planktonic creatures that it bounces into, and be fed upon by countless larger creatures. (Below). By the time a lobster reaches the third stage of larval development its tail fan is well developed, as are its swimmerets and claws. At this point in its life it is still planktonic and at the mercy of tide and current.

Innumerable fish feed on the drifting larvae. Unable to control their movement, the fry drift into anemones anchored to the bottom and onto jellyfish drifting through the water column. Some float out to sea to water too deep to settle in, and others drift too close to land, where they are caught in the surf and beached. If all that were not enough to wipe out the baby lobster population, they are also attacked in their free-swimming stages by everything from microscopic bacteria to sea birds.

Larvae in the Lab

One kind of bacteria, called *Leucothrix mucor*, has caused problems for researchers attempting to raise lobsters in confined areas. With many fry in a small volume of water, the bacteria spread rapidly and in some cases can cause the loss of an entire season's hatch of fry. What triggers the bacteria's growth in some years and not in others is not known.

When larval lobsters are raised in the lab, another problem arises which probably is not a factor in the lobster's survival at sea. The fry feed on each other. This has caused the nature of the lobster to be labeled cannibalistic. But lobster fry depend solely on chance to supply themselves with food. In the wild, whatever they collide with,

Anemones (sea animals that look like plants) are one of the dangers that face larval lobsters in the wild. Should the baby lobster fry drift into an anemone, the stinging cells on the tentacles will kill them. The tentacles then recoil, and draw the fry to the mouth at the top of the central stalk.

as they drift along, becomes a possible meal. In the lab where thousands of lobsters are packed together, they naturally collide with each other. And naturally they feed on each other. In the vastness of the sea, the fry may collide with each other but the chances are small that they will. Literally billions of other animals and plants make up the drifting living mass, called plankton, that the lobster fry are part of. The tiny lobsters have a much better chance of bouncing into a larval oyster, the planktonic stage of a striped bass, or a drifting bit of algae.

In the lab, to reduce this feeding-on-each-other, the fry are raised in circular tanks, in continuously swirling water to keep them separated. To reduce the problem further they are fed around the clock, every three hours, all through their larval development. Brine shrimp *(Artemia)* are what they are generally raised on. These are the same tiny shrimp that are fed to home aquarium fish by tropical fish fanciers. Frozen brine shrimp are used when space is not available to raise shrimp for live feeding. Young lobsters have also been raised on a purée of ground clams.

With the intense pressure of "cannibalism," predators, and bacteria, it is hard to imagine how many young lobsters survive. But the large number of eggs that the female lays ensures that a percentage will survive. That percentage is a small one though. Researchers estimate that less than one tenth of one percent of all lobsters hatched reach the crucial fourth stage of development. From hatching to the fourth stage only takes between 10 and 30 days, but it is a dangerous period for the fry.

Crucial Fourth Stage

The fourth stage of the lobster's life is crucial because at this stage, its appearance changes and the life it leads changes. During its first, second, and third stages it looks like a tiny insect and is at the mercy of tide and current. When it molts for the third time in its life and enters its fourth stage, it looks like a lobster and begins to act like one.

A first-stage lobster is beginning to feed on a weakened third stager. When many larvae are confined to a small volume of water, they sometimes feed on each other. This "cannibalism" probably does not occur in the wild.

Only about ¾ in. long (approx. 20 mm.), it has well developed pincers, a powerful tail, and long antennae. Instead of being attracted to the brightness of the surface, it is attracted to the dark of the bottom. Instead of drifting uncontrollably in the water column, it now has the ability to stay on the bottom and crawl about. Instead of relying on chance to supply it with food, it can now seek out its own. It is infinitely better equipped to manage successfully on its own on the ocean floor.

This fourth-stage lobster is reaching up to feed on a tiny brine shrimp. The young lobster is beginning to behave as it will for the rest of its life—staying on the bottom, seeking darkness instead of light, and actively seeking its own food.

3

Life on the Bottom

When the lobster molts again, it is in the fifth stage of its life. Metamorphosis is complete. The lobster is now on the bottom to stay.

Immediately after lobsters settle on the bottom though, they seem to disappear; many stay out of sight for years. Scientists are puzzling over where the lobsters hide to avoid predators. When plankton tows are made in a specific area, plenty of fourth-stagers, ready to settle on the bottom, can be found. And when scientists examine the bottom, plenty of four-year-olds can be found. But even when large pieces of the bottom are sifted and carefully looked at, there are few lobsters in between those stages.

Once lobsters are seen again, they have adapted completely to their environment. They prey on the animals that live on the sea floor with them, and behave like adult lobsters. They seek the security and darkness that crevices and holes can provide. Their nocturnal habits are fully evident. At night, they actively prowl the bottom searching for food, while during the day they remain quiet and inactive in their shelter.

Their Food

Often they return to their den with food to eat their meal at leisure, in safety, and in solitude. Hardly ever are two lobsters of the same size found in one hole. Lobster holes can sometimes be identified by the litter of past meals at the entrance.

Lobsters eat clams, mussels, snails, and marine worms. They also eat starfish, some seaweeds, and fish when they can get them. Lobsters are not scavengers in the true sense of the word, as they seem to prefer fresh food rather than decaying flesh. Many lobstermen claim they catch more lobsters when they bait their traps with fish that is a bit rotten. This is because the lobsters are attracted to the decaying bait, but they will not eat it.

This lobster is about to enter its fifth stage—it is spending much of its time on the bottom. How long it takes a newly hatched lobster to molt three times and reach the crucial bottom-settling fourth stage of development depends on many factors, water temperature being one of the most important. Generally the whole process takes between ten days and a month.

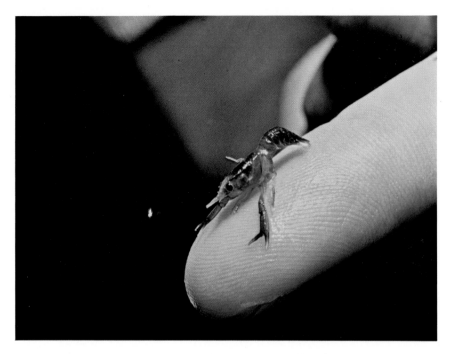

Lobsters are this size just after they settle on the bottom. This specimen is only slightly larger than the one on the opposite page. Because they have excellent methods of hiding from all the animals that feed on them, they are extremely difficult to find during their first years on the sea floor.

Favorite Meal

One of the lobster's favorite natural foods is the rock crab *(Cancer irrocatus)*. But a close relative of the rock crab, the Jonah crab *(Cancer borealis)*, is not eaten. When this crab is attacked it tucks its claws and legs close to its body and settles down into the bottom. The attacking lobster has nothing to grab, and eventually gives up. Rock crabs try to defend themselves when attacked, but they are no match for lobsters.

(Above). This lobster has just smashed the shell of a soft-shell clam. Hard-shell clams, mussels, snails, and marine worms are also eaten by lobsters. (Left). While the maxillipeds hold the clam in place, the other parts of the animal's mouth tear and grind at the food and move it into the animal's short esophagus.

Feeding Habits

When a lobster locates a meal, it uses almost all its appendages to eat. The lobster's large claw crushes and breaks the prey's outer covering or shell. The ripper claw tears at the flesh, and the pincers on the first set of walking legs bring the food to its mouth. The large appendages on each side of the lobster's mouth are called the maxillipeds; they hold the food in place while the other mouth parts work on it and bring it into the body for digestion. All this tearing, transferring, and grinding is not very efficient, and much of the food is lost to the currents and fish.

Jonah crabs (Cancer borealis) *are not part of the lobster's diet because when attacked they tuck in their appendages and settle into the bottom, giving the lobster nothing to grasp.*

Rock crabs (Cancer irroratus) *are a principal food in the lobster's diet because they try to defend themselves when attacked, and they are no match for a lobster.*

This lobster stands at the entrance to its burrow. It excavated the sand from between the large, growth-covered boulders, and now the burrow extends far behind the animal, deep into the rocks.

Shelter

After food, the most important element in a lobster's life is its shelter. On rocky bottoms, lobsters take advantage of the natural crevices and holes created by the jumbled rocks. In twisted and broken shipwrecks, lobsters can be found anywhere that the debris creates a tight pocket. They seem to prefer the tightest possible spaces.

For animals that seek the confines of a snug, dark shelter, you would not expect to find them on muddy bottoms. But, in fact, they do live in mud, burrowing tunnels in much the same way fresh-water crawfish burrow in river banks. Where no shelter is available, and the mud is too soft to hold a tunnel shape, lobsters will scoop out a depression in the mud and live in the concave hollow. This contradicts their basic need for confining spaces and they do this only when there is no other choice.

Lobsters do their burrowing and excavating either by "bulldozing," using claws and mouth parts to move bottom sediment, or by digging with their first three pairs of walking legs and fanning away debris with their swimmerets.

Sandy Bottoms

One kind of bottom that lobsters generally are not found on is one of plain sand or gravel. Because this kind of bottom lacks shelter and because they cannot dig their burrows in the shifting sand, lobsters will not stay on barren bottoms. Scientists are now at work trying to induce lobsters to live on sandy bottoms by providing them with artificial shelters. More about their work in Chapter 6.

The lobster's compound eyes sit on the end of movable stalks on each side of the animal's rostrum. This gives the lobster good vision to the side and back, as well as to the front. Compound eyes are made up of many light-catching elements over the curved surface of the eye while the eyes of most other animals consist of just one light-gathering lens.

This is the way lobsters move away from encounters with larger lobsters and preda-tors: close to the bottom, with antennae thrown back, and tail curled under, they slowly back away to shelter.

Daytime Habits

During the daylight hours, the lobsters are found in their burrows or caves, often at the entrance, waving their antennae, sampling the water for chemicals that might indicate the presence of an enemy or a particularly tempting bit of food. If threatened, they always retreat to the deepest, darkest recess of their hole. Often the hole seems to have a back exit for emergency escape, but these "back doors" are probably just a matter of natural bottom conditions rather than planned escape routes.

Retreat

Lobsters always back away from their attackers, leaving powerful claws facing their opponents. They throw back their antennae, curl their tail under their bodies, and slowly back away to the nearest shelter. Once lobsters are in their holes, they are very difficult to dislodge. First, they keep their claws facing the attacker. They also brace themselves by spreading their appendages to jam their joints

38

into the walls of their den. They also lift their bodies to jam their rostrums into the den's ceiling. The combination of jamming their rostrums, appendage joints, and all the short spines that point forward on the body makes it almost impossible to pull a braced lobster from its hole. This is why they prefer tight burrows which give the needed leverage to hold fast.

If a lobster is caught by surprise in the open and pursued by a powerful opponent, like a skin diver, it has a rapid method of escape. It can literally fly through the water by rapidly flexing its powerful tail. This rapid contraction of the tail muscle, more accurately the abdominal muscle, can send the animal through three to five feet of water in a flash.

Trying to grab a lobster without gloves can give you a lacerated hand if the lobster decides to snap its powerful tail. A lobster should always be held firmly about the mid-section behind the claws and should always be handled with caution. A large lobster's crusher claw can easily break a human finger.

When a lobster takes an aggressive, challenging posture, it stands high, raises its claws, and spreads its tail fan.

A

B

This sequence of photos shows a fourth-stage lobster using its powerful tail muscle to move backwards quickly. It is rapidly moving from left to right. Photo A shows the tail straight out. B shows the tail beginning the downward sweep.

Sampling the Water

As lobsters move forward, their antennae work rhythmically up and down, sampling the water as they move. Often, they actually touch the object under investigation, to identify positively what is sending scents or chemicals into the surrounding waters. They locate the source of scents by moving against the current, in the same way that land animals locate food and enemies from scents carried by the wind. The tiny hairs that bristle from the lobsters' legs and their other

C

D

In photo C the tail is almost completely curled, and in photo D the lobster moves to the right, too fast for the camera to stop the blurring of the claws.

appendages orientate them, line them up, with the current. Then their highly developed chemical receptors on their antennae, antennules, and other parts of their bodies, take over.

The lobster's eyes can rapidly adjust to the brightness of the surface or the dark of the bottom, but the images the lobster perceives are not sharp or well defined. A lobster can also receive some information through water vibrations. But the ability to single out and distinguish chemicals in the water is the lobster's greatest asset. It is through its chemical sensors that the lobster receives most of its day-to-day operating information. Lobsters actually communicate with one another through chemicals they release into the water. These chemicals, called pheromones, play very important roles in almost every phase of the animal's life.

Creatures that Prey on Lobsters

Aside from man, lobsters are preyed upon most heavily by codfish. Large cod average 10 to 25 pounds (5.4 to 13.7 kilos), and cods school in vast numbers over the same range as *H. americanus.* They feed on other crustaceans that live on the ocean bottom too, but lobsters are their favorite. Many other bottom-feeding fish also thrive on lobster, including blackfish, rockfish, sea robin, toadfish, sculpin, wolf-fish, eel-pout, goosefish, sand shark, and skate. Some lobstermen in Canada report that seals eat lobster too.

When lobsters are not evading their enemies they move along the bottom standing high on their jointed legs. They move forward, sometimes cautiously, sometimes rapidly, but rarely do they move sideways as their relatives, the crabs, do.

Codfish feed on a wide variety of bottom-dwelling crustaceans, but lobsters seem to be one of their favorites. Frequently cod are captured with their stomachs packed full of small lobsters that range from 1 to 3 inches (2.5 to 7.5 cms.) Cod are found in vast numbers throughout the same regions that lobsters occupy, so they influence greatly the size of lobster populations.

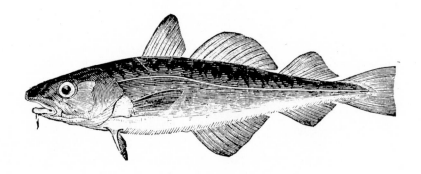

Toadfish, when they aren't biting each other, prowl the bottom for baby lobsters.

Sea robins use their finger-like rays to scratch loose animals that live in the substrate, including tiny lobsters.

Molting

As the lobster lives out its life on the bottom, it continues to grow and molt. During its first year on the bottom it will molt between six and nine times. The time of molting is extremely dangerous for the lobster. Immediately after it molts it is soft and flabby. The next 24 to 48 hours are needed for the lobster to harden its shell. It is completely helpless and vulnerable to the attacks of its enemies during this time.

43

Blackfish feed on many bottom - dwelling animals, including lobsters.

Sculpin range over the same areas as lobsters. They feed on many bottom-dwelling crustaceans, including lobsters.

Days before the actual molt process, the lobster's body begins to undergo change. Minerals from its shell are absorbed into its bloodstream, and its body functions slow down. It stops eating, moves little, and seeks a place to hide. When the molt comes, the lobster can do nothing to stop or reverse the process.

First Sign of Molting

First a crack appears across the back of the shell at the point where the tail joins the carapace. It is through this crack that the lobster will emerge. Lying on its side, and bending and arching itself, the lobster slowly pushes itself through the crack. The new lobster is almost

This lobster is in the process of molting. The lobster's old carapace has been pushed up, and the animal now is working its way out from under it, drawing its new claws out of the old ones as it does. Shortly it will begin to shed the old shell covering its tail. The blue pennant tag attached to the lobster here was shed with the cast-off tail portion of the shell just after this photo was taken.

folded on itself as it withdraws from the old shell. Once out of the shell, the lobster appears wrinkled and shrunken. It cannot move at all. If picked up at this point it would feel like a wet rag. Immediately, it begins to pump itself full of water, and within four or five hours it reaches its full new size.

Bluffing

Its claws are the last part of its body to be filled with water. As they attain their full size, the lobster begins to regain its mobility. Its shell is shiny and bright, and it looks like it is as hard as a normal lobster's. It is not. It is still very soft, but the hard appearance helps convince the lobster's enemies that it is not vulnerable. As soon as the lobster is able to move about, it immediately acts like its aggresive self in its encounters with other lobsters and predators. Usually the bluff works, but it takes about a week before the lobster has any real defense.

45

After Molting

Within two days after molting, it will have the stiffness of shoe leather, and in about ten days it will be back to its normal hardness. The cast-off shell is a perfect replica of the lobster and it is usually the newly molted lobster's first meal. Eating the old shell replaces minerals that might have been lost. Lobsters that eat their molt harden faster than those that do not.

Molting in the Lab.

In the laboratory, under the confining conditions of small tanks, when one lobster molts in the presence of another, it is immediately set upon, and eaten. But when two hard lobsters share a tank, though there is some pushing and shoving and raising of claws to establish which one will be "boss" of the tank, pitched battles are not continually waged. Usually the animal with the largest claws dominates the other.

A lobster's first meal, after it molts, is its cast-off shell. Minerals are put back into the lobster's system that would be lost if it did not eat the shell. Those lobsters that do not eat their shed shells take longer to harden.

In the wild, it is probable that lobsters do not attack each other while molting. In one experiment to find out, a large circular tank about 10 ft. (3 m.) in diameter, and 5 ft. (1.5 m.) deep, was set up to simulate bottom conditions. It was kept dark, supplied with plenty of food and shelter, and there were never more than four lobsters in the tank at any one time. Under these conditions, lobsters molting in the presence of more powerful animals were not attacked.

The molting process slows as lobsters get older. As they begin to reach sexual maturity, they molt only about once a year. Larger animals molt even less frequently, probably only once every few years. Animals in this category show that they do not molt often, as they carry on their shells growths of marine animals and plants. Large lobsters are often seen with fullgrown barnacles attached to their shells. Seaweeds, sponges, and mussels are frequently seen too.

Preening

Lobsters try to control the growth of such fouling organisms by preening. They are often seen picking over themselves with their second set of walking legs. This second pair of legs terminates in small claws through which the lobsters will often draw their antennae to rid themselves of parasites. With this second set of legs, the animal can also reach its compound eye to scrape it clean too.

No Terminal Molt

Unlike other crustaceans which stop molting, and therefore growing, once they reach sexual maturity, lobsters have no final or terminal molt. Because of this they grow to be one of the largest crustaceans in the sea. One of the largest lobsters ever reported lived at the edge of the continental shelf in over 1,000 ft. (300 m.) of water. It is believed to have weighed over 42½ pounds (19 kilos) and to have measured from the tip of its claws to the tip of its tail over 3 ft. (1 meter). As best as could be estimated it was between 50 and 100 years old. It is probable that larger lobsters have lived. There are unofficial reports of lobsters weighing as much as 50 pounds (23 kilos).

Mating

Molting is closely associated with mating. It is only when the female's new shell is still soft that two animals can copulate and start the process that will lead to a new generation of lobsters. Only 48 hours after molting, the female is too hard for penetration by the male's first pair of swimmerets, which pass the sperm into her body. Most molting occurs during the months of July, August, or September, depending on the water temperature that particular year. Males molt earlier than females, giving them time for their shells to harden so they will be able to mate successfully. They generally mate with equal-sized females, but small males can mate with larger females. When size differences are too great though, mating is not usually a success; large males cannot mate with smaller females.

In some areas lobsters reach sexual maturity just about the same time they reach the legal size limit fishermen can take. You will see in

This is a female lobster. Her first pair of swimmerets (a) are soft and feathery. At the base of her second pair of walking legs are the openings to the ducts from which she extrudes her eggs (b). Her sperm receptacle is between the last pair of walking legs.

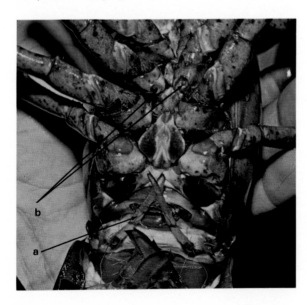

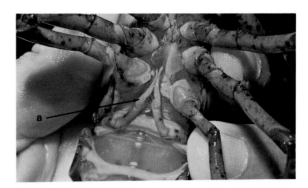

This is a male lobster. Its first pair of swimmerets (a) are hard and grooved to pass sperm cells into the body of the female. Note the sperm duct openings at the base of the last pair of walking legs.

Chapter 4 how this is affecting the number and size of lobsters caught each year.

Late summer, when most molting occurs, is also the best time for lobstering, because the population is active and moving about. As water temperature peaks, so does lobster activity. Much of the molting is by females that have just recently hatched their eggs after carrying them for a year. When they molt, males seek to mate with them. Some scientists believe that lobsters pair up two to three weeks before mating and remain together for about a week after. The many chemicals that are present in the water from all the molting females may explain the pairing and the high levels of activity.

When scientists try to mate lobsters in the laboratory, they introduce a male into the female's tank within a few hours after she completes the molt. The female ready for mating releases pheromones into the water that attract and excite the male. Some of the other pheromones tell the male of her soft condition. Because she is newly molted and soft, her partner must be gentle.

Courtship Dance

The partners begin what has been described as a "courtship dance." Coming head to head, each turns around slowly and they come head to head again. During the "dance" the male continuously strokes the female with his antennae. They separate, then come together again, this time with the male behind the female. After following the female

Lobsters mate soon after the female molts, while her shell is still soft. "Courtship" can last as long as half an hour, but once the animals are together, copulation only lasts about a minute. In the photo the male is on top of the female.

around the tank, the male gently climbs up her back and then turns her onto her back with his walking legs. She extends her large claws straight out in front of her so they will not be in the way as she is rolled over. The two are now in close contact. While the other swimmerets beat to keep him in position, the first pair, which are hard and grooved, deliver the sperm to the sperm receptacle of the female. This final phase of mating lasts only about a minute. The whole sequence can last as long as half an hour.

The female will keep the sperm alive within her body through the winter and spring and extrude her eggs in early summer. The eggs will stay under her body for almost a full year, and then on some warm night in June, when the clocks in her body say conditions are right, she will hatch her brood. As they drift away into the black open sea, the cycle begins again.

Man The Predator

When we think about one animal preying on another we sometimes forget to include ourselves in the picture, but in the case of lobsters it is impossible to exclude man. Without a doubt, man preys most heavily on lobsters.

From an animal that was not highly regarded as a food item a few hundred years ago, the lobster has progressed to a point where it is a highly desirable luxury food, very much in demand. When the first settlers of the coast of North America came across the Atlantic, they found lobsters in numbers they had never seen in Europe. Lobsters piled the beaches in such vast numbers that they were used to fertilize crops. Only servants, slaves, and the poor ate lobster regularly.

The Early Fishery

By 1800, though, the picture had changed somewhat. Enough people were eating lobster to make it profitable for some fishermen to confine their work exclusively to lobster traps, or "pots." Until then, lobsters had always been caught incidentally while fishing for other species. This early lobstering started along Cape Cod and the Massachusetts coast.

The two "eggers" caught in the traps in the background must be returned to the water. For every "egger" a lobsterman keeps, he can be heavily fined. Worse though, by keeping lobsters with eggs he greatly diminishes the number of lobsters available to him in the future.

It was after 1850 that the fishery began to expand, particularly along the coast of Maine. And, by 1870, enough people in the United States were eating lobster to signal the rapid expansion of a Canadian fishing effort. The bulk of Canadian-caught lobsters has always been exported to the U.S.

In the late 1880s lobster production reached its peak in both the U.S. and Canada, but for the next 75 years the lobster landings declined with all-time lows during the 1920s and 1930s. Soon after World War II lobster landings began to rise again.

Catch information shows, to a degree, what is happening to the total lobster population and recent catch data indicates the lobster population is declining. Dramatic increases in efforts to catch lobsters have yielded only a small rise in the total number of lobsters landed. For example, during the 1950s about 40 pounds (18 kilos) of lobsters were caught per trap set over a period of a year. During the 1960s, the catch per trap set per year dropped to less than 30 pounds (13.6 kilos). During the 1970s it fell to about 15 pounds (6.8 kilos).

52

Scientists in the U.S. and Canada who are taking the pulse of the lobster population say the patient is sick. Each year more traps have to be set to catch the same number of lobsters, and each year the average size of individual lobsters caught shrinks. In 1873, off New Brunswick and Nova Scotia the average lobster caught weighed between 2½ and 3 pounds (approx. 1.2 to 1.5 kilos). That is about three times the average size of lobsters from the same area today.

In the United States today, the average lobster caught is just barely the legal size, which varies from area to area. What is even worse, ten lobsters have to be trapped before one that is of legal size can be found. It is good that the various states have established laws to protect egg-bearing and young lobsters. But the sad part is that the laws are often broken, difficult to enforce, and in regard to young lobsters, the laws do not protect them before they mate.

The easiest and most accurate way to measure a lobster is to measure the length of its carapace. That is the distance from the base of the animal's eye socket to the point where the flexible tail joins the hard shell. Most female lobsters do not mature until they reach a carapace length of about 3⅞ in. (98 mm.). The laws today that are supposed to protect the stock are inadequate.

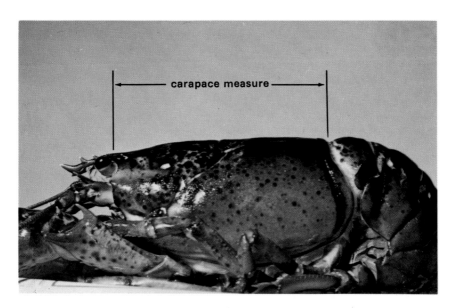

carapace measure

Lobsters are measured from their eye sockets to the end of their carapace. The legal minimum in most areas is 3¾6 in. (81 mm.). It has been proven though that most female lobsters do not reach sexual maturity until they are about 3⅞ in. (98 mm.) in carapace measure. This means that most lobsters taken legally have not mated. Although in some areas, such as Long Island Sound and certain areas of Canada, female lobsters reach sexual maturity at about 3¼6 in.

Lobsters under 3⅞ in. (98 mm.) are the future breeding stock of the population. Their removal can only lessen the total number of lobsters in the future. A selection process is going on which selects for young breeders those animals that mature and mate early in life. The young lobsters carry fewer eggs, a smaller total number survive, and in the end the whole population declines.

Increasing the size limit on lobsters taken, to give them all at least one chance to mate, is one thing almost all scientists agree on. And all agree that efforts to do so must be undertaken soon if the lobster population is to recover from the overfishing that has reduced it.

Pollution

In addition to overfishing, man is affecting the lobster population in another way—through pollution of the ocean. Larval lobsters are particularly vulnerable to the effect of even tiny amounts of crude oil or oil distillates in their environment. Concentrations of crude oil as low as one tenth of one percent will kill lobsters in each of their four floating stages. Lower concentrations cause them to develop abnormally as they progress from one stage to the next.

Small amounts of kerosene confuse the mature lobsters' chemical receptors. Low concentrations cause them to begin searching for food when none is present. Crude oil, in concentration lower than one hundredth of one percent disturb the animals' feeding habits too. This tiny amount of oil doubles the time it takes for a lobster to notice the presence of food and go after it.

Despite the heavy fishing pressure and the effects of increasing pollution, the lobster fishery is still the most important fishery for both the U.S. and Canada in the North Atlantic region. Some scientists are working to help the fishery maintain that position, while others are exploring different methods to ensure that there will be enough lobsters for everyone to enjoy.

This lobsterman is measuring the just-caught lobster to see if it is big enough to keep. Unfortunately, even if the lobster is "legal," it probably has not had a chance to mate.

Aquaculture Experiments

Many scientists have been applying their knowledge to the problems of raising lobsters commercially. They are trying to raise lobsters in ways similar to the way chickens and beef cattle are raised—on a large scale for commercial markets. But raising an animal underwater, especially when the animal has a complex life cycle, sloppy feeding habits, and a pugnacious nature in close confinement, is no easy task.

At the Massachusetts State Lobster Hatchery on Martha's Vineyard, lobsters have been successfully taken through their complicated life cycle. There, egg-bearing females regularly hatch thousands of young lobsters, some of which are selected to be raised to full-size adults. Experiments at raising lobsters began soon after the hatchery opened its, doors, in 1949. But because of limited finances, mass rearing was never possible. The work at the hatchery, though, has provided invaluable information and the techniques learned there have become models for many other projects that have been able to secure funds.

Engineering Approach

Scientists are approaching the problems of mass lobster culture in a number of different ways. One group is taking an engineering approach. These scientists are working with the animal as it is, realizing that it will have to be continually separated from its fellow crustaceans. They are building automated systems that will feed the animals from modified poultry feeders and keep the lobsters apart with a system of pens that can be expanded as needed. These scientists are also using increased water temperatures to speed growth. Starting with egg-bearing lobsters they believe they will harvest lobsters of 1—1½ pounds (453–680 grams) in 2 to 3 years, as opposed to the 6 to 8 years it takes for a lobster to attain that weight in the wild.

Breeding Approach

Some scientists believe that the only way to mass culture lobsters is to breed a docile animal that can be kept in close quarters with others. While breeding lobsters with this docile quality, hopefully they could breed them for fast growth, double crusher claws, wide tails, and disease resistance. Scientists are selecting young lobsters with these qualities, raising them to maturity, then mating them with lobs-

This experiment was designed to find how much room a lobster needs to grow best, without wasting space. Each compartment contains a lobster, some having more room than others. Scientists are finding that lobsters grow fastest when they can move in an area about three times their body size. With less space they grow slower.

Note that this lobster has two crusher claws instead of the usual arrangement of one crusher and one ripper claw. The animal was caught in the wild this way, but attempts will be made to mate this male with a double-clawed female with the hope of raising a domestic breed of lobsters with two crusher claws. Lobsters so endowed have 15 to 20 per cent more meat than normal animals.

ters of similar disposition and anatomy. The biggest problem to this approach is the time it takes to bring each generation to maturity. Even with raised water temperatures, it takes between two and three years. And there is no telling how many generations would have to be developed to get the desired results.

Slow as this method is, it is probably the most sound. It is the way all animals have been domesticated. One question everyone is asking, though, is: after all this genetic scrambling, will the lobster taste good?

Behavior Modification

Another group of scientists are looking toward chemicals to modify lobster behavior. At times during the lobster's life it loses its pugnacious tendencies, most notably at the time of mating. Mating occurs when a male encounters a newly molted female. Under similar circumstances, if a hard lobster is confined with a newly molted animal, the soft animal is attacked and eaten. The female ready for mating, though, communicates this to her mate and is not harmed. She communicates with her mate by releasing pheromones into the water. Researchers believe that if the pheromones causing the changes could be isolated and introduced to confined lobsters, they might reduce the attacks on molting animals.

These lobsters, each about 1½ in. (38 mm.) long, are separated because at this stage they molt frequently. If all were raised together, eventually there would only be one animal left—the biggest.

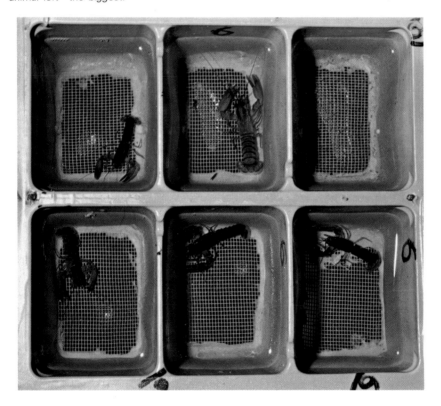

Pond Culture

Still other scientists want to explore the possibility of raising large numbers of lobsters in closed ponds with circulating sea water. Giving the animals plenty of food and shelter, they want to see exactly what problems molting animals cause in high density situations. They think that with adequate food, shelter, and space, lobsters could be raised in ponds with a minimal amount of handling and man-involvement.

There is a market for more lobsters than the fisheries can supply. And if the price of lobster were lowered there would be an even larger demand. Whether or not lobsters can be raised in large enough numbers to be profitable is what these experiments are trying to determine.

Fishery Experiments

Until aquaculture becomes a reality, everyone will have to get along with the lobsters that the fishery can supply. Some scientists are helping fishermen improve their catch of lobsters. They believe that by studying the lobster in its natural surroundings and carefully watching where and when lobsters move, they will be able to tell lobstermen what months are best for lobstering and where the best spots are. Many lobstermen know much of this information from generations of fishing experience, but generally they do not know the reasons why lobsters act the way they do. Cooperating with scientists, the lobstermen supply facts they have learned through experience, live animals for research, and any unusual specimen they come across while fishing. Marine biologists try to supply reasons for lobsters being in an area one year and not there another. They also try to give reasons for dwindling annual catches, and try to predict future catches.

Tagging Experiments

Tracing the underwater movements of lobsters is an important job. With movement information, scientists are able to predict where to find lobsters. Lobster movements are traced in the same way that fish movements are traced—by tagging. Scientists try to tag lobsters as soon as they are captured and release them close to the point where they are found. Most often the animals are brought to the surface, tagged, and released. Some scientists though are taking their equipment underwater and tagging the lobster there.

When the tagged lobsters are recaptured, the person that caught the lobster notes the time, date, and location of the catch, and sends that information to the address on the tag. When the scientists receive the catch data, they send the person their reward and information about the tagging project.

After hundreds of such transactions, maps tracing movements can be drawn, and eventually the whole picture of lobster activity comes into focus.

Many different kinds of tags are used. One of the simplest consists of an information disc with a rubber band attached. The rubber band hooks over the animal's rostrum and clips to the end of the carapace. The problem with this tag is that when the animal molts, it leaves the tag with the old shell.

Another kind of tag stays with the animal through three or four molts. It is anchored in a muscle of the animal that is under the carapace, and leaves a plastic pennant, with return information, extending between the carapace and the tail.

No method of tagging lobsters exists that will identify an animal for life. Many methods have been tried, including punching holes in the tail fan, removal of swimmerets, and even branding. None of the techniques are totally effective.

Natural Tags

At the Massachusetts State Lobster Hatchery on Martha's Vineyard, workers are raising brightly colored lobsters in an attempt to solve the problem. Unusually colored lobsters occur in the wild, but not in great numbers. At the hatchery, the researchers select from broods of thousands those animals with unusual pigmentation, and then raise them under carefully controlled conditions. As these animals mature, they are mated with animals of the same color to produce strains of indigo blues and orange-reds. Spotted lobsters are sometimes produced too—these are called calicos. These distinctive animals could be used as "natural tags," their color identifying them for life.

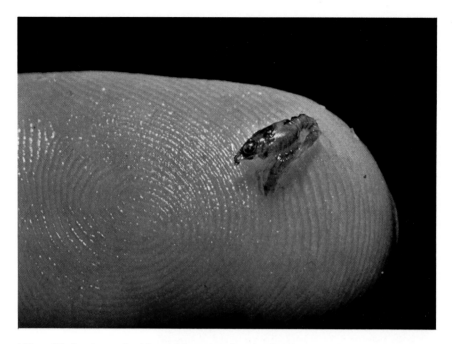

When this hatchery-raised larval lobster reaches its fourth stage of development, it will be released into the waters close to the spot where its mother was found. With luck, it will survive and settle on the bottom, increasing the number of lobsters available to the local fisherman.

Pigmentation

In the wild, most lobsters are dark green with touches of red, a mixture of their natural pigments: red, blue and yellow. Theoretically lobsters can be raised in each of their principal pigments and in any combination of them too. When a red lobster is mated with a normal lobster, 50 percent of the offspring are red, 25 percent have normal pigmentation, and the remaining 25 percent are albino or colorless.

While all this work goes on, much is being learned about the genetic make-up of lobsters. That information will be invaluable as more attempts are made to raise lobsters commercially.

Migration

Right now tagging devices are the principal means scientists have for keeping track of lobster movements. It was through tagging experiments that researchers at the National Marine Fisheries Service deter-

This is a lobster's normal color. The pigments in the animal's shell are red, yellow, and blue. When mixed, they produce the color shown.

This red lobster is the offspring of a normal male and a red female. From that mating 25 percent of the young were of normal color, 25 percent albino, and the remaining 50 percent red, similar to this one.

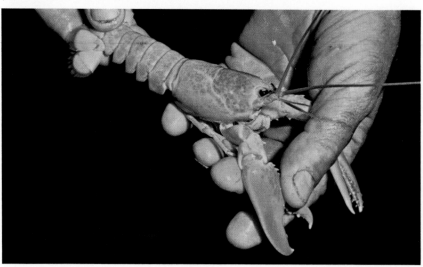

This is an albino lobster, its shell completely lacking pigmentation. Albinos could be used as "natural tags" for tracing lobster movement, but their unusual brightness might subject them to high predation.

Blue lobsters are found in the wild, but this one was selectively bred for its pigmentation as part of the genetic experiments being conducted by scientists at the Massachusetts State Lobster Hatchery.

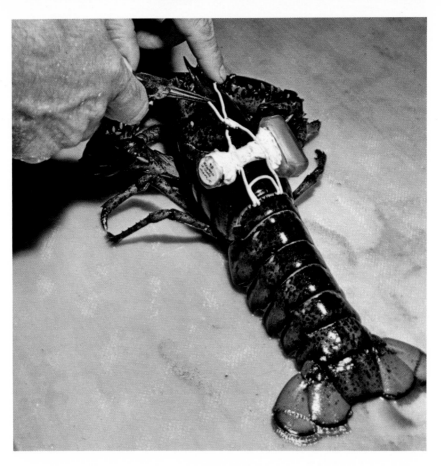

This sonic tag is being used by scientists to keep track of the local movement of lobsters. The tag emits a signal to a team of scientists in a boat on the surface where it is interpreted and plotted on a chart. Experiments with tags like these have shown that lobsters spend a few days in one burrow, move to another, and then move again, somewhat like "musical chairs." It has also been learned that lobsters have extraordinary navigational abilities.

mined that off the coast of North America there seem to be two separate lobster populations with very little intermingling. After years of work and over 5,000 lobsters tagged, they have determined that one group of lobsters inhabits the deep waters at the edge of the continental shelf and that the other group inhabits the shallow coastal waters of the U.S. and Canada. So far the scientists have found that the two groups differ in only one way. The inshore population does not migrate, while the offshore group is almost continually on the move.

The offshore populations live in water as deep as 1,500 ft. (450 m.), and are generally larger than their inshore relatives. The tagging experiments have shown that the offshore animals prefer warm water. In summer, as the shallow water warms, the offshore populations move toward it, and in effect toward the land. In winter, as the shallow water cools, they move back to the edge of the continental shelf where the deep water is actually warmer than the water close to land.

Local Movement

While the inshore populations do not migrate with changing temperatures, their local activity is greatly affected by temperature. When they are active, they move quite a bit within a small area, usually within a circle of one mile (1.6 km.) radius. Locally their movement is somewhat like "musical chairs." They inhabit one burrow for a few days at a time, then move on to another for another short stay. Often they return to a burrow that serves as something of a "home base."

Details about the local movements of the inshore lobsters have been under study by workers at the University of Connecticut. They have found that lobsters seem to have extra ordinary navigational abilities. Lobsters can leave their burrows at night, hunt over a featureless bottom as much as ¼ mile (400 m.) away, and return over the same courses to their burrows before dawn. Anyone who has been underwater at night on a barren bottom knows that is quite an accomplishment. The researchers have made these discoveries by mounting lobsters with special tags that emit electronic signals. The signals are picked up on the surface by a team that plots the movement information on maps of the bottom. The sonic tags are often attached to the animals underwater to disturb them as little as possible. The tags are compact and fit snugly on the lobster's back.

Colonization

Tagging is one way scientists help fishermen, but another group of scientists believe they can help lobstermen in a different way. At the University of Rhode Island, researchers feel they can best help the fishery by introducing lobsters to areas where they generally are not found—on sandy bottoms. They believe that by providing shelter in areas where none exist, they can induce lobsters to settle there. Adding shelter to an area should increase lobster survival and increase the over-all population. Because lobsters seek darkness and tight spaces, the scientists are dropping small specially shaped concrete structures on open stretches of sandy bottom. Some of the structures are shaped like domes, others are box-shaped, and still others look like sections of pipe.

Within a few months after being placed on the bottom, the shelters become covered with mussels, sponges, and seaweeds. They would appear to be part of the natural bottom if they were not spaced evenly in specific patterns for the experiments. But even before the shelters begin to blend into the bottom, lobsters move in.

In one experiment near Point Judith, Rhode Island, almost 400 shelters were placed on a sandy bottom, and within three weeks over

Much can be learned about lobsters by studying their movement; however, because they molt frequently conventional tagging devices do not work. A tag placed on the lobster would be lost the next time the animal molts. No method of tagging lobsters exists that will identify an animal for life. Some scientists are raising brightly colored lobsters in an attempt to solve this problem.

This lobster is occupying a shelter that was built by scientists and placed in an area where lobsters normally are not found. The shelter, made of concrete, is now covered with tiny mussels and other marine animals. Even before it became covered with growth, though, the lobster moved in. By providing shelters like this, scientists hope the overall lobster population will expand and that new areas will be opened to lobstering.

80 percent were occupied by lobsters. Most were juveniles, but the researchers feel providing shelter for young lobsters may be just where the shelters do the most good. Experiments off Block Island have been successful, too. One set of shelters, after only two weeks on the bottom, had about 40 percent habitation with a good mix of lobsters—a large egg-bearing female, many just short of legal size, and a few palm-sized juveniles.

69

Different factors affect how many lobsters move into the shelters and how fast. Proximity to a natural population, season, distance between shelters, and shelter shape all play a part.

More ambitious plans to introduce lobsters to areas where they do not occur naturally have been tried, but with only limited success. In 1847, the U.S. Fishery Commission began transplanting *H. americanus* to the Pacific coast of the U.S. Over the next forty years, experiments continued sporadically, and transplants were placed in the Monterey area, in Puget Sound in Washington, and in Yaquina Bay in Oregon. All attempts failed to create a West Coast population and the project was eventually discontinued.

Since 1954, the Canadians have been trying to introduce *H. americanus* to their Pacific coast, off British Columbia and around Vancouver Island. They believe they are beginning to achieve some degree of success because young lobsters, hatched from East Coast transplants, are beginning to turn up.

7

Lobsters Around the World

Around the world *Homarus americanus* has many relatives. Some look very much like the lobster that inhabits the waters off the eastern edge of North America. Others are not similar looking at all, but they are in the same biological groupings of crustaceans and decapods. One thing they all have in common is their powerful tail muscle (actually their abdominal muscle) which they all use to escape quickly from their enemies. It is this muscle that is sought for food by people around the world.

The closest relative to *H. americanus* is *H. gammarus* (sometimes called *H. vulgarus*). Its life habits are almost exactly those of its American counterpart. Living in the cool waters off Northern Europe, it looks exactly like the American lobster except it is darker in color—more green and sometimes almost black. It is found around the British Isles, where it is called "lobster," around Germany, where it is called "hummer," and around northern France, where it is called "homard."

Another animal that lives in these same Northern European waters, and looks like a delicate version of the common lobster, is the Norway lobster. *Nephrops norvegicus* is also called the "Dublin Bay prawn" when caught near Great Britain. It is about 7 in. (180 mm.) long when fully grown, and has long slender claws that are almost as long as its body. It burrows on muddy bottoms in water 60 to 800 ft. (18 to 240 m.) deep. It is also found in the Mediterranean, where it is called "scampi."

71

Spiny lobsters are by far the most numerous of all the animals grouped under the name, lobster. They live in just about every tropical and subtropical sea around the world, and are easily identified because they lack the great claws of *Homarus*, and have long thick antennae. They get their name because their bodies are dotted with tiny sharp spines.

Most spiny lobsters belong to the genus *Panulirus*, in which there are about a dozen species. The spiny lobsters that live in the Mediterranean and around the southern areas of Great Britain belong to the genus *Palinurus*. The similarity of the names always creates problems for students studying spiny lobsters.

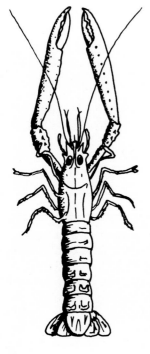

(Left). Norway lobsters inhabit waters all the way from North Africa to Iceland and Norway, but they are most abundant in the North Sea where they are heavily fished by France, Britain, and Denmark.

(Opposite page). At night the spiny lobsters leaves its cave to seek food. It leads a nocturnal life just as its relatives in cold water do.

(Above). Under the protecting ledge of part of a coral reef off the Florida Keys, sits a spiny lobster, Panulirus argus. During the day, these animals remain in their caves and move little. Sharing the coral's shelter with the spiny lobster are some sponges, sea urchins and a hatchet fish.

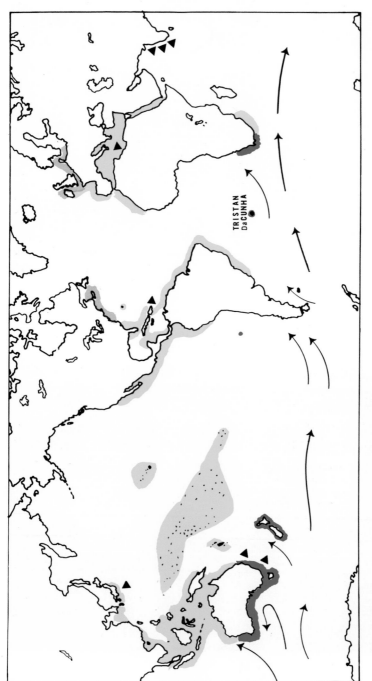

Distribution of some of the animals around the world that are known as "lobsters."

Key: *Homarus* (true lobsters) ■
Panulirus and *Palinurus* ▨
(spiny lobsters, warm-water varieties)

Jasus (spiny lobsters, cold-water varieties) ▨
Scyllarus (sand, shovel-nose and locust lobsters) ▲
Antarctic currents ➤

TRISTAN DaCUNHA

(Above). These spiny lobsters, Palinurus elephas, inhabit the waters of the eastern Mediterranean. Their spine-covered carapaces and mahogany color distinguish them from spiny lobsters in the genus Panulirus. (Below). The spiny lobster, Panulirus argus, has fewer spines on the carapace and lighter coloration. These animals inhabit the waters of the Caribbean and the Florida Keys.

Some spiny lobsters also live in cold water. Icy currents that stream north from the Antarctic bathe the west coast of South Africa, southern Australia, New Zealand, some islands off Chile, and Tristan da Cunha in the South Atlantic. In these regions the spiny lobster is *Jasus*.

Spiny lobsters are known around the world by many names. Some of the more common ones are: *langouste*, rock lobster, crawfish or crayfish. The terms crawfish and crayfish, though, are confusing because true crawfish live only in fresh water. True crawfish are found all over the world in the muddy banks of lakes, streams, and rivers. There are many species, but they all belong to either the genus *Astacus* or *Cambarus*. To add to the confusion, true crawfish look like small duplicates of *H. americanus*.

This is not a young lobster—it is a full-grown true crawfish. Crawfish are fresh-water animals that live in burrows in muddy banks of rivers, streams, and lakes in just about every country in the world. This particular kind of crawfish, Cambarus, *can be found all over the eastern United States.*

Spanish lobsters, locust lobsters, shovel-nose lobsters and sand lobsters are some of the names for the creature above. Scientifically they are classed in the genus Scyllarus. *Found in warm waters around the world, they inhabit the same areas as spiny lobsters. They are not nearly as common, though.*

Migration

Some spiny lobsters behave in a very unusual way at certain times of the year. During the late summer and early autumn they make mass migrations. In the waters around the Bahamas, thousands of lobsters have been observed making their way along the bottom, forming living rivers. They move constantly day and night, they eat very little while on the move, and they never seek shelter. Whether they form these massive chains to mate, to move to warmer waters, or to seek new hunting areas, is not known. This behavior contradicts all that is known about spiny lobsters, and scientists are studying the phenomenon now.

This is one of the larval stages (greatly enlarged) that spiny lobsters go through before they settle on the bottom. After hatching, the tiny spiderlike larvae drift in the water column. They pass through as many as twelve stages before they settle on the sea floor.

This is another larval stage that spiny lobsters go through before they settle on the ocean floor. When they finally do settle on the bottom they are about 7/8 in. (28 mm.) long and totally transparent. As they molt they become reddish brown in color.

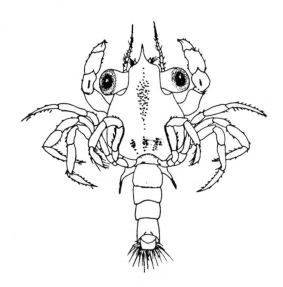

78

This palm-sized spiny lobster (Panulirus argus) *developed from a floating planktonic animal that looked like a spider. It went through many complex changes each time it molted until it looked like a smaller version of the animal shown here, and settled on the bottom.*

Aquaculture Experiments

Scientists are also studying spiny lobsters to see if they can be raised by man under controlled conditions. One portion of the animal's life cycle is presenting many problems–the larval stage. Unlike *H. americanus,* which has only four planktonic stages, spiny lobsters have a long and complex larval development. Some species have as many as twelve delicate spidery stages to go through before they settle on the bottom. Keeping the larval lobsters alive in the laboratory through these delicate stages is very difficult. Few spiny lobsters have been raised to maturity from eggs in the lab.

Other relatives of *H. americanus* that live in the same areas as the spiny lobsters are called locust lobsters, sand lobsters, shovel-nose lobsters and Spanish lobsters. They all belong to the genus *Scyllarus* and there are many species. Their flattened paddle-like antennae give the whole animal a strange shape, sometimes making it difficult to distinguish one end from the other. Though their range is world wide, they are not common anywhere.

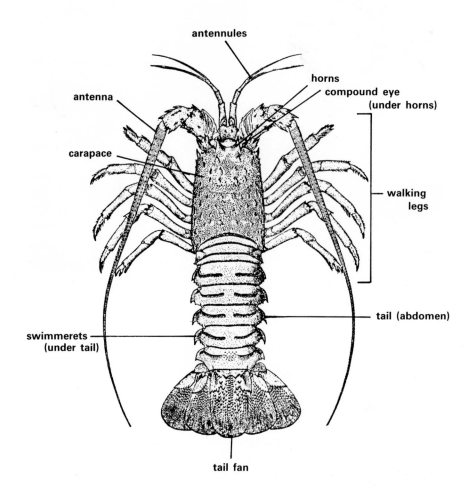

antennules

horns

compound eye
(under horns)

antenna

carapace

walking
legs

tail (abdomen)

swimmerets
(under tail)

tail fan

Spiny lobsters are covered with tiny sharp projections on their carapace, their antennae, and parts of their tail. They also have segmented tails (abdomens) and jointed appendages (their legs and swimmerets are examples). These two characteristics place the lobster in the phylum Arthropoda. *It is in the class of animals called* Crustacea *because of its hard shell (or exoskeleton). Also, because it has ten walking legs it is in the order* Decapoda.

This spiny lobster is Justinia longimanus. *Its very long antennae are one of the features that aid in identifying it. All spiny lobsters have long, flexible antennae which they use to ward off prey. Spiny lobsters also use their antennae to keep scavenger fish away while they feed. The antennae are covered with tiny spines and are effective weapons.*

Florida Population

Fishery scientists are studying the spiny lobster in Florida to determine if the populations there are stable enough to maintain their
present numbers if fishing pressure continues to increase. Part of
their work will determine if the mature lobsters found in Florida
were hatched in Florida waters or elsewhere in the Caribbean.

Around the world there are more than 30 species of lobsters with claws that resemble H. americanus. This species is presently unidentified. It was found in 30 ft. (10 m.) of water near the island of St. Croix in the U.S. Virgin Islands. It was about 6 in. (150 mm.) long and was observed to be active at night.

Because lobsters go through many floating stages it is possible that the lobsters found in Florida waters were actually hatched as far south as Venezuela, Columbia, or Brazil in South America. Coastal currents and the Gulf Stream could bring the drifting larval lobsters north to Florida.

If new lobsters join the Florida populations in this manner the policies that the fisheries' scientists will establish will be different than those established if the local population is self-sustaining.

These maps show the two ways that the spiny lobster population off Florida may be sustained. Fisheries' scientists are now conducting experiments to determine which way is correct. In the Closed System young lobsters hatch and grow to maturity in Florida waters. In the Open System larval lobsters drift up from South America with prevailing currents and then settle on the bottom in Florida waters. The young of those animals may in turn drift out into the Atlantic to populate the waters around Bermuda.

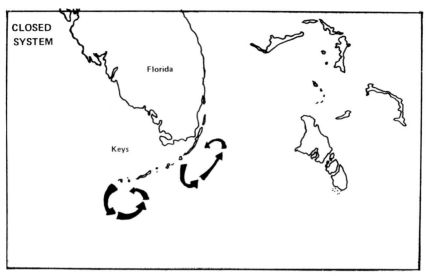

CLOSED SYSTEM

Florida

Keys

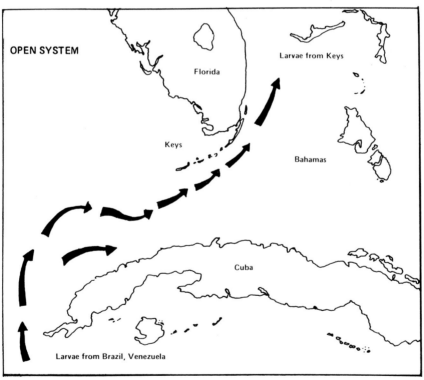

OPEN SYSTEM

Florida

Keys

Larvae from Keys

Bahamas

Cuba

Larvae from Brazil, Venezuela

83

Besides the well developed tail muscle, all the relatives of *H. americanus* have one other thing in common—they all taste delicious. Each region claims its native lobster is best, but that is a matter for gourmets to decide. Hopefully the research going on now will provide information that will ensure the debate's continuation. If all goes well, perhaps lobsters will be on the planet as long as man.

Afterword

When the original edition of this book was published almost ten years ago, it discussed a problem that fishery scientists had been grappling with for years: The lobster fishery off the northeastern coast of the United States was in trouble.

The fishery was (and is) experiencing problems because the American lobster is fished very intensively throughout its range. Because of this most of the lobsters caught have never had a chance to mate and reproduce, even one time.

Although the number of lobsters caught has remained relatively constant, the catch per unit of effort has steadily declined through the past 25 years. Simply stated, it takes more time and work to catch the same number of lobsters.

To add to the problem, the fishery has expanded to include the offshore population. For many years that lobster population had not been exploited. With this offshore population now under pressure, too, it can no longer act as a buffer and support the intense exploitation of the inshore fishery.

That was the bleak picture ten years ago and, unfortunately, that is the situation today.

However, things are changing. The biggest problem in regulating the fishery has been political. Each state in which lobsters are caught has had its own regulations, and because of the economic importance of the fisheries to each state regulations often were made in response to local pressure. Thus any conservation measure by any one state was undermined by others since fishermen from different areas often fish the same lobster population.

But the good news is that a new regional program for the conservation of lobsters will come into effect over the next few years and it will be managed under federal jurisdiction. The following is a summary of that plan.

Summary of The American Lobster Fishery Management Plan

The American Lobster Fishery Management Plan was developed by the New England Fishery Management Council to establish a coast-wide lobster management program under federal control. Regulations to implement the plan were published in the *Federal Register* on August 10, 1983. The plan will promote consistent coast-wide management of this valuable fishery. Many of the measures are already imposed by the coastal states where lobsters are landed. The measures mentioned here are scheduled to take effect over a period of three years. The measures and their effective dates are as follows:

Effective September 7, 1983: Landing or possession of lobster meat will be prohibited. Lobster parts may be landed (until January 1, 1986) provided that the sixth tail segment measures at least 1 1/16 in. (26 mm.) in length and that not more than two claws are landed with each lobster tail.

Landing of female lobsters bearing extruded eggs will be prohibited, as will the removal of such eggs or the possession of lobsters from which eggs have been removed.

Vessel owners intending to fish for lobster in the Fishery Conservation Zone (FCZ) (from 3 to 200 miles offshore) will be required to obtain permits issued by the National Marine Fisheries Service (NMFS) or through cooperative agreements with the coastal states. NMFS will attempt to establish cooperative agreements with each state before the start of the 1984 fishing season. Until that time, as a matter of practicality, a valid state lobster fishing license will be sufficient for fishing in the FCZ. After January 1, 1984, state licenses will only be accepted for FCZ fishing if the license is properly endorsed and issued under a cooperative agreement. After Janury 1, 1984, fishermen who wish to apply for a lobster permit should contact their state marine fisheries agency to determine whether a cooperative permit program is in effect for their state. Any fisherman may also apply directly to NMFS for an FCZ permit.

Effective January 1, 1985: All lobsters landed whole must meet a minimum carapace length of 3 3/16 in. (81 mm.). All traps must be vented to allow release of sublegal lobsters and be marked with the owner's identification.

Effective January 1, 1986: All lobsters must be landed whole. Landing or possession of lobster parts will be prohibited.

A copy of the complete federal lobster fishery regulations may be obtained by writing to the National Marine Fisheries Service, State Fish Pier, Gloucester, Massachusetts 01930.

Clawed Lobster Regulations by State*

	ME	NH	MA	RI	CT	NY	NJ	DE	MD	VA	NC
License Requirements											
No license required							X		X		X
Required to fish lobster	X	X	X	X	X	X		X		X	
Required to land lobster	X	X	X	X	X					X	
Required to deal in lobster	X	X	X	X	X						
Legal provisions for Aquaculture											
Enterprises	X	X	X	X	X	X	X				
Fishermen Classification											
None							X		X	X	X
Commercial	X	X	X	X	X	X		X			
Non-commercial		X	X	X	X	X		X			
Catch/Effort Reporting											
Not required							X		X	X	X
Required annually	X	X	X			X	X		X		
Requires daily record				X	X						
Gear Regulations											
None							X		X		
By license class:		X	X	X	X	X				X	
Quantity allowed		X	X			X				X	
Type allowed	X	X	X			X		X			
Owner identification required	X	X	X	X	X	X		X			
Escapement opening in devise catching specified	X		X	X				X			X

Clawed Lobster Regulations by State*

	ME	NH	MA	RI	CT	NY	NJ	DE	MD	VA	NC
Fishing Activity Regulations											
None											
By license class or method:			X	X		X		X			
number of licences			X								
Catch quotas						X		X			
Area	X	X	X			X					
Season	X		X					X			
Day or time of day	X	X	X	X	X			X			
Landing of lobster meat regulated	X	X	X	X	X	X		X	X	X	X
Landing of lobster parts regulated	X	X	X	X	X	X		X	X	X	X
Landing of gravid female lobsters prohibited	X	X	X	X	X	X	X	X	X	X	X
Landing of V-notched female lobsters prohibited	X										
Landing of lobsters regulated by size (carapace length)	X	X	X	X	X	X	X	X	X	X	X
5 in. maximum allowed	X										
$3\frac{1}{16}$ in. minimum allowed											
$3\frac{1}{8}$ in. minimum allowed		X					X				
$3\frac{3}{16}$ in. minimum allowed	X		X	X	X	X		X	X	X	X

*These laws are changing. See the accompanying information.

Florida Spiny Lobster Laws

1. Do not take more than 24 lobsters per day per boat.
2. Do not take crawfish that have less than a 3 in. (7.6 cm.) carapace or 5½ in. (14 cm.) tail (tails may not be separated from the body while on the water).
3. Do not take egg-bearing female lobsters.
4. Take lobsters only by hand. Do not use gigs or spears.
5. The season for lobsters runs from August 1 through March 31. No lobsters can be taken from April through July.

California Spiny Lobster Laws

California's open season on spiny lobsters for sport divers runs from the first Wednesday in October through the first Wednesday after March 15. Note the following:
1. The legal bag limit for divers is seven lobsters, each one at least 3¼ in. (8.25 cm.) long measured in a straight line on the midline of the back from the rear edge of the eye socket to the rear edge of the body shell.
2. Every person taking lobsters must carry some device capable of measuring their size accurately.
3. No undersized lobster may be brought aboard any boat, placed in any container, or retained in anyone's possession or under his direct control.
4. Divers may take spiny lobsters only by loop net or by bare or gloved hand.
5. A California sportfishing license is required.
6. No lobster fishing is allowed in the Heisler Park Ecological Reserve off Laguna Beach; in the San Diego-La Jolla Ecological Reserve; at Lovers' Cove Reserve at Santa Catalina Island; at the Point Loba Reserve in San Diego County; and at Abalone Cove Ecological Reserve in Los Angeles County.

The Department of Fish and Game cautions sport divers that laws against the robbing of commercial lobster traps will be strictly enforced.

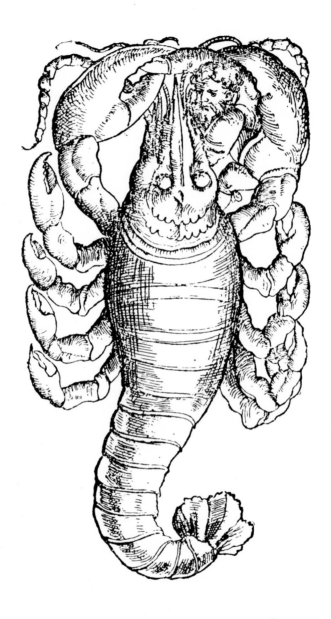

In the 15th century, Olaus Magnus wrote that in the waters between Orkney and Hebrides Islands there lived lobsters large enough to catch swimmers and squeeze them to death in their claws. He probably was exaggerating.

Index